Potty Poets

Vikings Don't Wear Pants

Vikings
Don't Wear Pants
Potty Poems of the Past

by
Roger Stevens
and
Celia Warren

Drawings by Michael Leigh

The King's England Press
2001

ISBN 1 872438 73 3

Vikings Don't Wear Pants is typeset by Moose Manuscripts in
Tempus Sans ITC 14pt and published by
The King's England Press Ltd,
Cambertown House, Commercial Road, Goldthorpe,
Rotherham, South Yorkshire, S63 9BL

Printed and bound in Great Britain by

Woolnough Bookbinding
Irthlingborough
Northamptonshire

About the Authors

Roger Stevens

I've always been fascinated by the gory goings on in our dim and distant past. When I decided to write this book of poems I soon discovered just how grim, grisly and ghastly our ancestors were. So nothing much has changed really, has it?

Celia Warren

I grew up in the era of the Beatles, mini-skirts and elephant jokes and, just as man was taking his first small step on the moon, I was narrowly scraping a pass at 'O' level history - another gigantic leap for me towards this, your verse history book. Enjoy!

Michael Leigh

Dedicated to
my favourite historical relics, my parents.
For Mary and Raymond Barker,
with love and thanks from
Celia

For Pat and Roy,
who will never be past it.
With love,
Roger

Vikings Don't Wear Pants
Roger

Vikings wear tough chain mail,
With noseguards quite advanced,
And metal goggles for their eyes
But Vikings don't wear pants.

Some Vikings wear silk shirts to work
And, given half a chance,
A lovely brooch to clasp their cloaks
But Vikings don't wear pants.

Some Vikings did wear underclothes,
Their legs they might enhance,
But boxer shorts or Y-Fronts? No!
Vikings don't wear pants.

So when you meet a Viking
And he swears and raves and rants,
Is he a wimp or is he tough? Check!
Is he wearing pants?

Aztec Treats
Roger

Frogs were tasty, ants were yummy,
Locusts, they used to rate them.
They kept as pets, dogs without hair
And when the dogs got old, they ate them.

Equus
Roger

The Emperor Caligula
Was mad, of course.
To help him rule he promoted
To the Senate, his horse

The horse was good and just
But rather negative, they say,
For in big debates the horse
Would always answer, "Neigh!"

['Equus' is Latin for 'horse'.]

One Previous Owner (Probably)

Celia

Lost your teeth? Find it hard to chew?
Ugly gaps left you defaced?
No problem! Fresh from Waterloo –
Have your teeth replaced.

Guaranteed fit for the task;
Will not rattle!
Neat, discreet, no questions asked,
(Fell off the back of a battle!)

[After the battle of Waterloo, teeth were removed from the skulls of the dead lying on the battlefield to be recycled.]

9

Football Through the Ages
Celia

Football grew from itchy feet
Kicking whatever they found in the street:
A pebble, a stick, a rolling stone,
A clod of clay or an animal's bone.
The left-over bladder of a butchered pig,
Inflated and tied off, was perfect to kick.
If something would roll it would do for the game
Which then had not even been given a name
Till, on through the ages, the game was to grow,
At long last becoming the football we know.
Oh, I'm glad of my football, I'm glad of the rules,
I'm glad of the pitches at clubs and at schools.
I'm glad of my kit, but I am even gladder
The days have long gone when they kicked a pig's bladder.

Stone Age Remedy

Roger

So, you have a headache?
No need to scream and shout.
I'll drill a hole into your skull
And let the headache out.

Those spirits, trapped, will surely flee
Once your noddle has been vented;
I would give you an aspirin, too,
But they haven't been invented.

*[Drilling a hole in the skull was called trepanning and is
still used by some doctors today. Don't try this at home!]*

On Track
Roger

In eighteen twenty-five
At Darlington Station
Some passengers wait for a train.
Says Samuel, "I see that the six forty-three
From Stockton is late again."
The stationmaster says, "Sorry –
Blame the cow who strolled on the line.
I'm sure that we'll soon get the hang of this thing
And in the future trains *will* run on time."

Please May I Be Excused?
Celia

What did people do
Without the modern loo?

Ancient Romans thought
To set holes in their fort
Above the moat, and got 'em;
A sponge on a stick,
That did the trick,
To wipe a Roman bottom.

(No swimming in the moat!)

Pharaoh Nuff

Celia

Deep inside a pyramid, crawling on my tummy, I came across a sarcophagus; inside it was a mummy. I asked, "What's your name? Can I join you in bed?" One answer he gave, "Two-Kan-Kum-In," he said.

Bert the Bloodthirsty Barber

Roger

Snick, snack, snick, snack,
It's Bert the Bloodthirsty Barber.
He'll trim your hair in the shape of a ship
And your beard in the shape of a harbour.

Snick, snack, snick, snack,
He's a whiz with a needle or razor,
He'll lop off the wart from the end of your nose
And chop off your mouldy old toes, Sir.

Sir Walter Raleigh

Roger

> *"And curse Sir Walter Raleigh*
> *he was such a stupid git."*
> *- John Lennon, commenting upon Raleigh's*
> *introduction of tobacco to England.*

In the Tower of London,
Where the walls of stone
Are as thick as a pharaoh's tomb,
Sits Walter Raleigh, all alone,
Where the ghosts of the Princes
Murmur and moan,
And he stares into the gloom.

He dreams of the days
When he travelled the seas
Far and wide to exotic shores,
He discovered potatoes,
Tobacco to smoke
And everyone said, "What a jolly good bloke!"
But they don't say that any more.

Now they say that he plotted
Against Good Queen Bess,
Now his friendship with her has gone sour,
So he sits and he writes to pass the time,
And occasionally pens
An amorous rhyme,
Condemned for life in the Tower.

No Smoking

Celia

Before the invention of plastic
False teeth were not much good.
First, they were carved from animal bone,
Later, made of wood.

And those who liked a cigarette
Would certainly avoid
The earliest of plastics,
Inflammable celluloid.

One man set his teeth on fire,
It's perfectly true - no joking!
After that his choice was clear:
No teeth or no more smoking!

In the Trenches
Celia

Spirits cruelly dampened in the trenches,
Strong men cried and glory lost its shine,
Songs died on their lips, the music faded
With images of loved-ones left behind.

They had no choice but to share their rations
With rats, and observed their cunning skill;
The rodents learnt to pierce the tins on *both* sides
To guarantee a flow of Nestlé's Milk.

No words do justice to the pain and killing,
The misery of the trenches and the squalor,
But, for a moment, one man paused to marvel
At the rat's resourceful mind amid the horror.

Navy Blues
Celia

Hauled by horrible, hairy hands
Out of *The Horse and Hound*,
Through the squelchy, slippery mud
Across the roughest ground.

Down the gravelly, grimy hill,
Around the giant rocks,
Over the stony harbour wall,
Into the dingy docks.

Up the rough and raggedy rope
I'm dragged aboard a ship:
The Press Gang caught me unawares
To join their ocean trip.

Goddess – Handle With Care
Roger

The goddess Coatlicue
(Huitzilopochtli's Mum)
Was a hit in the fashion stakes,
She wore a striking full-length skirt
Made up of poisonous snakes.

That's Showbiz

Roger

The lion leapt, I dodged, I danced,
I struck the creature with my lance.
His claw drew blood.
I winced, I cried,
I held my side.
He leapt again, I dodged, I ducked,
I threw my net and caught his mane
And with my lance
I cancelled out my debt –
The lion died.

I heard the crowd roar,
Cheer, applaud.
I looked to Caesar, saw him frown,
His hand extended,
Thumb held...

(Or, if you prefer a happy ending,,,,)

I looked as Caesar raised his cup
Of wine. He smiled,
His thumb held…

The Three-Hundred-Year Journey of Oliver Cromwell's Head

Celia

They dig up Oliver Cromwell,
They dig up Cromwell's mates
And string them high in Tyburn, but,
For Cromwell, there awaits

A special treat, though, if he knew,
He might not really like
To have his rotten head chopped off
And stuck upon a spike.

It's by Westminster Abbey,
Where people point and stare
And, after over twenty years,
Cromwell's head's still there.

Then, in 1685,
Winds carry it away.
A sharp guard picks it up and saves it
For a rainy day.

He hides it up his chimney,
A secret for some years
Till, at a dreadful freak-show,
Cromwell reappears.

From hand to hand the head is passed,
A lucrative concern;
No dignity for Cromwell,
Nor grave in which to turn!

At last a Dr Wilkinson
Acquires the famous head;
He keeps it tucked inside a box,
Wrapped in black and red

Until, in 1960,
It finally gets passed
To Sydney Sussex College
Where they bury it, at last.

ENTER IF YOU DARE

2/6D

CROMWELL'S
'ORRIBLE
HEAD!

Splitting the Atom
Celia

It took a lot of thinking,
It almost burst the cranium,
To find out how to split the atom
Present in uranium.
Those who'd said, "It can't be done!"
Their words went down the dranium.
A concept hard to understand
And tricky to explanium,
Nuclear power, good or bad,
Is here to remanium.

You Don't Taste Very Well

Roger

To some, a visit to the loo
Is simply to get rid of waste,
But to doctors in Ancient Rome
This was not the case.
They believed that in testing urine
The cause of your ills could be traced,
So they checked the smell and the colour,
But most of all the taste!

Henry the Eighth
Roger

Henry the Eighth
Was a fat old king
Tariddle tariddle taree.
He liked to eat
And he liked to sing
Fol diddle fol diddly fol dee.

"I'm too fat to climb
The stairs," he said,
Tariddle tariddle tareech.
So with pulleys and ropes
They winched him to bed
Fol diddle fol diddly screech.

He wrote *Greensleeves*
For his girlfriend, 'tis said,
Tarridle tariddle taronk.
When his wife found out
He cut off her head
Fol diddle fol diddly bonk!

Please May I Be Excused?
Celia

What did people do
Without the modern loo?

Holes in the ground
The Tudors found
Seemed rather like mistakes.
They were a joke
And yet some bloke
Decided to call them jakes!

(Jake can keep them!)

Roman Invasions
Celia

BC55

Julius Caesar,
Roman geezer,
Came to Britain,
Wasn't smitten,
Back to Gaul
After all.

AD43

Emperor Claudius,
More maraudius,
Had his reasons,
Sent more legions.
They were stronger,
Stayed much longer,
Long enough
For roads and stuff,
Built some baths,
Had some laughs,
England greener
Greater, cleaner!

[I made up the word maraudius. Well, Shakespeare was always making up words, so why shouldn't I?]

For Five Farthings

Roger

Riding a bike
In Victorian times
Was not a lot of fun;
Over cobbles and stones
It shook your bones
And gave you a very sore bum.

But riding a bike
In Victorian times
Was a craze that spread like wildfire
When, in 1888,
John Dunlop created
The first ever blow-up tyre.

Shoe the Blues Away

Roger

A little known fact:
When King Tut had the blues
He'd choose one of his hundred
Pairs of shoes.

On a Tudor Flea
Celia

When divers raised the Mary Rose,
Little did those men suppose,
Amongst the treasures of the sea,
Preserved for our posterity,
That they would find a tiny flea:
A Tudor flea that took to sea
In fifteen-forty-five;
A tiny mite whose dying bite
Made history come alive.
Preserved in silt, within the hold,
Alongside plates and tools and gold,
Tucked within a garment's fold,
Four centuries it lay,
Until the day we gazed amazed
At one small flea's tremendous age:
A parasite to behold!

[When the wreck of the Mary Rose, sunken flagship of Henry VIII's fleet, was raised, amongst the treasure and everyday articles which came to light, preserved in the sea-bed silt, was a tiny flea. This flea is displayed today, behind the lens of a magnifying glass, in a Portsmouth museum.]

Dead as a Dodo
Celia

They say what starts well ends well,
But for the dodo on Mauritius,
End it sadly diddid
For its start was inauspicious;
Unable to fly, it was bound to die,
(Did they eat it? And was it delicious?)
How sad to think it's now extinct,
A no-no on Mauritius!

THE DODO

[The flightless, defenceless dodos were all killed off by 1681.]

The Magna Carta

Roger

Old King John
Was a terrible King
And a terrible King was he.
He fought his dad and killed his nephew
And ruined this fair country.

The barons said,
"It's gone to his head!
On this we all agree.
This behaviour must stop
Or we'll give him the chop
For ruining this fair country."

Now old King John
Had a terrible rage
And a terrible rage had he.
And he said rude words
But the barons had swords
So King John had to agree

To sign his name
To the Magna Carta
Which was a Royal Decree,
That the law everywhere
Would be just and fair
And thus save this fair country.

Old King John
Was a terrible King
On that all must agree,
But because he signed
On the dotted line
We now live in a land that's free.

The Knitting Club
Roger

Click, click, click, click,
Knit one, purl one,
Knitting my nephew
A cardigan.

There goes another one,
Sneezing in the basket.
Wonder what it was he'd done?

Swwwiiissshhh!
Ooooooooohhhh!
Clunk!
Plop!
Aaaaahhhhhhh!

This new guillotine,
She's better than the old one;
The blade was getting rusty,
Didn't always cut clean.

Click, click, click, click,
What are you knitting, Annemarie?
Ah, mon ami, did you see that?
The executioner, he smiled at me.

Here comes today's last prisoner,
Then we can all go home

Swwwiiissshhh!
Ooooooooohhhh!
Clunk!
Plop!
Aaaaahhhhhhh!

Time to get the supper on.

[During the French Revolution a group of women used to go to executions at the guillotine, taking with them their knitting to make a day of it. They became known as the Knitting Club.]

At the Tower of London
Celia

Some people say the ravens stay
To keep the Tower from falling,
But ravens cackle at the thought,
So fruitlessly appalling.

Ravens at the Tower
Remember what they like,
And every day they hope and pray
For heads upon a spike.

Their ancestors have told them
How good Queen Bess supplies
Fleshy heads for ravens
To peck away the eyes.

The birds patrol the Tower,
Anticipate no less,
And so they stay and think each day,
Today's the eyeballfest!

Yes, ravens at the Tower
Remember what they like
So they will stay and hope each day
That Queen Bess hasn't gone away,
They'll call and caw for evermore
For heads upon a spike.

Old Sam Morse

Celia

Old Sam Morse he had a code
di di di di di di dah dah dah
And in that code he had some dots
di di di di di di dah dah dah
With a *di di* here
And a *di di* there
Here a di, there a *di*
Everywhere a *di di*
Old Sam Morse he had a code
di di di di di di dah dah dah

dust to dust
ashes to ashes
may we always remember
his dots and dashes

1791 - 1872

Old Sam Morse he had a code
di di di di di di dah dah dah
And in that code he had some dashes
di di di di di di dah dah dah
With a *dah dah* here
And a *dah dah* there
Here a *dah,* there a *dah*
Everywhere a *dah dah*
Old Sam Morse he had a code
di di di di di di dah dah dah

A Happy Childhood
Roger

If you were a child
In Aztec times
You definitely had to behave
Whilst cleaning the house
And working the fields,
Or you might be sold as a slave.

If you were a child
In Aztec times
It was definitely not very nice;
In times of drought
Or famine,
You might end up as a sacrifice.

In England's Green and Pleasant Land

Roger

In England's green and pleasant land,
In forest, field and spa,
There echoes round the hills a sound:
Aaaaaaaaaaaaaaaaahhh!

In ancient times, if Stone Age tribes
Wandered just too far,
An argument would soon break out and:
Aaaaaaaaaaaaaaaaahhh!

When Roman legions came to Kent
And said, "How fair you are.
But why have you painted your faces blue?
Boudicca said, "Aaaaaaaaaaaaaaaaahhh!"

When William landed on the beach
His men said, "Ooh, la la!"
Then shot their arrows in the air;
King Harold cried out, "Aaaaaaaaaaaaaaaaahhh!"

I sometimes think the human race
Has not come very far.
I'd throw those hawks and warmongers
Into a deep pit –
Aaaaaaaaaaaaaaaaaaaaaaaaaaaaahhhhhhhhh!

A Liking for the Viking
Celia

I've always had a liking for the Viking:
His handsome horns, his rough and ready ways,
His rugged russet hair beneath his helmet
In those metal-rattle, battle-happy days.

I've always had a longing for a longboat,
To fly like a dragon through the sea,
To peaceful evenings round a real fire,
Alive with legend, rich with poetry.

I've always had a yearning for the burning
Of brave flames irradiating valour,
For the fiery longboat carrying its Chieftain
To his final feast in glorious Valhalla.

All Wright in the End
Celia

Contraptions that flapped
And tried to be birds
With scaffolding wings.

Constructions so weird
That they defy words,
With pedals and springs.

There were many attempts at powered flight
Before Orville and Wilbur got it Wright!

Romans on the March
Celia

Left, right
Left, right
Left, right
Left, right
Left, right
Left, right
Left, right
Left, right
   Sinister, dexter
  Sinister, dexter
   Sinister, dexter
HALT!

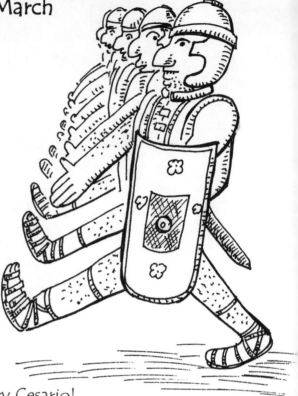

No skipping, Legionary Cesario!

And...
Left, right
Left, right
Left, right
Left, right...

*[The Romans must have got very bored walking along
the very straight roads they always built. 'Sinister' is Latin
for left and 'dexter' for right.]*

The Yeoman of the Stool

Roger

At being a lowly servant
I was such a great success;
I've been promoted to serve the King,
King Henry VIII, no less!

I am the Yeoman of the Stool
And this is what I do:
I fetch the Royal Chamber Pot
When King Henry wants a poo.

It's like an ornate wooden box
And inside is a potty;
The seat is padded velvet
For the King's most regal botty.

Yes, I am the Yeoman of the Stool,
A courtier of note;
And when the King has finished
I tip the contents in the moat.

First Class Poem
Roger

A letter dropping through
The letter box
Is always a thrill;
God bless
Sir Rowland Hill.

Reading the Entrails
Roger

The priest pulled
From the dead sheep's body
Its blood-soaked intestine
And proclaimed:

"The sun will shine upon
Your son and daughter,
The clouds will rain
Upon your vines and crops."

("Excuse me,
Now I need
Some soap and water."

"Lots.")

44

The Bayeux Tapestry

Celia

Oh, William, what a Conqueror!
I'm proud of you and itching
To show you this fine tapestry
The girls and I are stitching.

There's you, my hero, and the boys
Giving Harold's lads a pasting,
I've sewn the arrow in his eye
Where Harold fell at Hastings.

It isn't finished yet, my dear,
My needle needs new thread,
It takes a lot of sewing
Showing oh-so-many dead!

When you see the size of it,
The horses, men and spears,
All carefully sewn, you'll understand
Why it's taking years.

But, William, I'm so proud of you,
Can't wait for you to see
Your own victorious battle-scene
Portrayed in tapestry.

BAYEUX

The Curse of Osiris

Roger

A million suns
Had blazed across the sky,
A million moons
Had bathed the shifting sands
With their reflected light,
As deep beneath the pyramid
The young king Tutankhamun
Dreamed of stars that shone
Upon an endless night.
When Lord Carnarvon,
Howard Carter and their crew
Discovered Tutankhamun's tomb
They little did suspect
That, by disturbing Tutankhamun's rest,
They would release the Curse of Osiris
To dog their every step.
A snake ingested Carter's pet canary
And then each day an accident or some
Strange death. And five months on
The cursed Carnarvon died and, it is said,
His faithful terrier in England, far away,
Howled to the moon and also dropped down dead.
Coincidence?
You may be right.
But tell me why the lights of Cairo all went out
Upon that fateful night?

T.F.I. Friday

Celia

It's been a long week in the longboat
And the oarsmen's arms are aching,
It's hot inside their helmets
And the Viking heads are baking.
They've pillaged and they've plundered
And, by Thor, those men have thundered!
But now, at last, their Chieftain cries,
"Oars down! And leave them tidy!
You've all done very well, my lads,
But now, thank Frigg, it's Friday!"

*[Frigg was the Viking god of love. No wonder the day
we all love was named after her!]*

Whatever Next?

Roger

I heard a funny tale today
(That Copernicus, he's a one)
He tried to make us all believe
The Earth goes round the sun.

You can see the sun moves round the sky,
It needs no explanation.
Copernicus is a lovely bloke
But he's two stars short of a constellation.

[Nicolaus Copernicus was a Polish astronomer who, in the 16th Century, tried to convince everyone that the Earth moved around the sun. What a preposterous thing to say!]

The Grocer's Apprentice

Roger

Oh, to be an apprentice,
Only fifteen and working hard;
I wake at dawn, clean up the shop
And wash my hands in the yard.
*(In the summer I wash my feet, too ,
And I have an all-over bath once a year.)*

Beer and bread for breakfast
Then we open the shop again;
Sugar from the Turkish Empire
And pepper stolen from Spain.
*(Those Spaniards don't like to tangle
With Francis Drake!)*

I go to bed as darkness falls,
Under the counter I sleep;
Oh, to be an apprentice,
Working six days every week.
(But I get Sundays and Christmas Day off.)

There are riots on the streets of London
And everyone has to run
When the Watch is called with their muskets and pikes,
But a lad's got to have some fun.
*(There are puppet shows over the river
But Southwark's a real dump.)*

What's in a Name?
Celia

The history of old England
Extends beyond a book,
You can read it on the pub signs
Everywhere you look.

The Yew Tree is a relic
Of medieval days,
It provided wood for longbows
Or was planted over graves.

When James the VI of Scotland
Was England's first King James,
The Red Lion of his heraldry
Was favourite of all names.

The Punchbowl Inn sign swings from pubs
Whenever it is windy;
'Punch' means 'five' (ingredients),
The word is 'pac' in Hindi.

When people had to travel far
They'd often hire a horse,
At which inn would they find one?
The Nag's Head, of course.

The Chequers comes from Roman times,
The chess-board of old games,
Or money-changing business
Might have given inns these names.

If you read the pub signs,
Everywhere you look
You'll find old England's history
Extends beyond a book.

Stone Age Misfit
Celia

There once was a cave man who fainted
Every time anyone painted
Scenes on the wall
Of his cave. Above all,
It was pictures of hunting he hated.

An Accident Waiting to Happen
Celia

Before the days of motorways
Or man's first driving test,
The internal combustion engine
Didn't always bode the best.

It may have been invented with
The finest of intentions,
But horseless carriages – really!
What hazardous inventions!

So, ten steps in front of them,
Walked a man with a bright red flag;
A sensible precaution,
Though to some it seemed a drag.

At last he was disposed of,
The motoring law was bagged,
But we wouldn't have motorway pile-ups now
If we'd kept that man with the flag!

King Canute
Roger

Once more on to the beach, dear friends, once more
And fill our boots up with this English sand.
You say I am a God that could command
The sea itself to back away from me? Let's see –
And make today a day that no one will forget!

He tried. He failed. And everyone got wet.

[Canute did this to prove that he was merely a mortal like everybody else.]

Watch Out! Monsters About

Roger

I wouldn't go on that ship, mate,
I wouldn't go on that craft;
That Christopher Columbus,
He's having a bit of a laugh.

He's off to the edge of the world, mate,
If you go on that ship you will die;
You'll sail right over the edge, pal,
And fall into the sky.

That's if you're not eaten by dragons, mate,
Sea monsters with terrible breath,
Looking for sailors like you, pal,
To lure to a fiery death.

It's going to be some voyage, mate,
Sailing the ocean blue.
What's that? Am I going? Of course, pal,
What else can a sailor do?

Poor Old Phoebe!

Celia

Some thought her a god
And worshipped her on their knees,
Others, not so kind,
Said she was made of cheese
Until, in 1969,
Without so much as a pretty please,
They walked all over her, even cut
Pieces from her lunar gut.
Yet still she shines
In poets' lines,
None of her romance gone,
Despite being trodden upon.

[Phoebe was the Ancient Roman name of the Goddess of the moon, also called Artemis in Ancient Greek legend. Often, the name Phoebe is used poetically to mean the moon.]

I Don't Like Tournaments
Celia

I don't like tournaments,
I'm hopeless with a lance;
I'll never win a maiden's hand,
I shan't get the chance.

I don't like tournaments,
The trumpet's far too loud,
My horse gets terrified
And charges in the crowd.

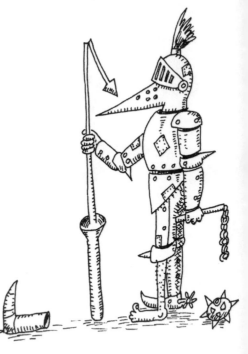

I don't like tournaments,
I often drop my shield
And spend ages afterwards
Searching through the field.

I don't like tournaments,
I always lose the glove
Of the maiden I most fancy
And then I lose her love.

I don't like tournaments,
I'm hopeless with a lance
But, at least, without a maiden
I won't have to dance!

(I don't like dancing, either!)

The Boil on a Viking's Bottom

Roger

In the top ten ailments of times long past
(And be glad you never got 'em)
The wart on a Roman's nose is top
And the boil on a Viking's bottom.

Pit Boys
Celia

Easy come, easy go,
London slums, full of woe.
Down the pit
Children fit,
In the mud they go.

Down, down, the deep, dark hole,
Pushing heavy trucks of coal,
Harry, Dick or pauper Tom,
Plenty more where they came from!

Crawling under dripping ceilings,
Never mind the children's feelings;
Starving pit-boys have no voice,
Beggars never have a choice.

Easy come, easy go,
London slums, full of woe.
Down the pit
Children fit,
In the mud they go.

Dodgy Diogenes

Roger

I have no use for a house, you see,
No table, no chairs and no bed;
I don't need a palace of finely-cut stone
Or even an old timbered shed.

No table, no chairs and no bed,
I never have friends round to dine;
My home is a barrel with room for just me
And it's based on the snail's design.

I never have friends round to dine,
A barrel's not roomy, in truth,
Though the top can be used as a table
If you like to eat from the roof.

A barrel's not roomy in truth,
I have no use for a house, you see
We come into this world with nothing,
And nothing's enough for me.

[Diogenes was a Greek Cynic philosopher who lived in
Athens from 400 to 325 BC and preached that everyone
should live a very simple and uncluttered life.]

Leonardo da Vinci

Celia

Fifteenth century helicopter
Sketches by da Vinci
Shows he thought that folk would fly,
In fact he was convinci.

He watched the world of nature,
Saw winged seeds that danci,
Based on observation,
His drawings were advanci.

Engineering and inventing
And art were his provinci,
He would have been so very keen
On rockets, would da Vinci!

If he had lived five hundred years
He might have had the chanci
To be the first man on the moon.
Instead he died (in Franci).

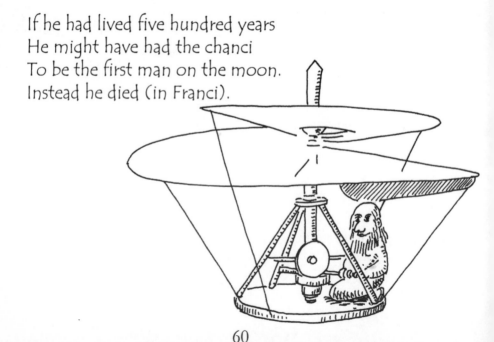

60

Please May I Be Excused?
Celia

What did people do
Without the modern loo?

Regency beaus
Performed on peaus;
(That's 'chamber pots' in French.*)
It was quite absurd
To disguise the word
And it didn't hide the stench.

(Potty, if you ask me!)

But that's what people had to do
Without the modern loo.

*[*Actually, it's not. The word 'peau' in French means skin, but if I'd written 'pots' it wouldn't have looked right.]*

Alfred The Great

Roger

"I'm popping out for some cheese,"
Said the cow girl, "Please
Keep an eye on the meat and the bread."
But Alfred was thinking
About his Kingdom shrinking
And didn't hear a word she said.

The bread started to burn
As the cow girl returned.
She said, "I wasn't gone long.
Are you the kind of bloke
Who thinks it's a joke?
Didn't you notice the pong?"

Alfred picked up his sword
And said, "'pon my word!
But I didn't burn the gravy."
Then he gave a loud shout,
Kicked the Danes out,
And established the English Navy.

Votes For Women
Celia

Please go to the polls,
Don't veto your vote,
Your right to be counted
Was dearly bought
By valiant women,
Each brave Suffragette,
So use your vote wisely,
We owe them a debt.

They chained themselves up,
Fought to the last breath,
One dived at the King's horse,
Got trampled to death.
They protested with placards,
"Votes for Women!", they said,
Then, in prison, were brutally,
Forcibly fed
When on hunger-strike; some
Were left practically dead.

So go to the polls,
Don't veto your vote,
Your right to be counted
Was dearly bought.
Please use your vote wisely,
Help repay the debt
We owe to the women,
Each brave Suffragette.

With Thanks to:

Eve and Adam, without whom this book would not have been possible, and Debbie, Steve and Phil, for making it happen.

Acknowledgements

The following poems have been previously published: **Football Through the Ages** in *We Was Robbed,* chosen by David Orme (Macmillan, 1997); **Pharaoh Nuff** in *Fairground Toast and Buttered Fun,* Celia Warren (The Lichfield Press, 1996); **Equus, Grocer's Apprentice, Sir Walter Raleigh** and **Henry VIII** in *Hysterical Historical Poems*, chosen by Brian Moses (Macmillan, 2000).